# I.S.Q.D.

## Identification System for Questioned Documents

*By*

**BILLY PRIOR BATES, A.B., M.G.A., LL.B**

HV
8074
B38

**CHARLES C THOMAS · PUBLISHER**
*Springfield · Illinois · U.S.A.*

*Published and Distributed Throughout the World by*
CHARLES C THOMAS • PUBLISHER
Bannerstone House
301-327 East Lawrence Avenue, Springfield, Illinois, U.S.A.
Natchez Plantation House
735 North Atlantic Boulevard, Fort Lauderdale, Florida, U.S.A.

This book is protected by copyright. No part of it may be reproduced in any manner without written permission from the publisher.

© *1970, by* CHARLES C THOMAS • PUBLISHER

Library of Congress Catalog Card Number: 70-105625

*With* **THOMAS BOOKS** *careful attention is given to all details of manufacturing and design. It is the Publisher's desire to present books that are satisfactory as to their physical qualities and artistic possibilities and appropriate for their particular use.* **THOMAS BOOKS** *will be true to those laws of quality that assure a good name and good will.*

*Printed in the United States of America*
N-10

# Preface

QUESTIONED DOCUMENT IDENTIFICATION has two essential parts: *discovery* and *proof*.

The purpose of this manual is to put at the fingertips of the investigator a scientific method of the discovery of the fact and the proving of it.

Part I of the manual, which places handwriting identification on a laboratory basis, along with fingerprint and voiceprint identification, presents the scientific comparison of a questioned writing with the genuine.

Part II of the manual deals with the preparation of the facts for presentation and the method of presenting them to those who legally are to decide the matter in court.

Part III offers a sample demonstration of the discovery and proof of the fact, which gives the investigator a concrete application of I.S.Q.D.

It is not within the scope of this manual to discuss the properties of writing materials or the other aspects of the field of Questioned Documents. These are left to the trained examiner to handle for himself. Only the method used in Graphoanalysis for comparing *strokes* of a handwriting, and the demonstration of them as the basis for the handwriting examiner's opinion, is considered.

B.P.B.

LIBRARY
STEPHEN F. AUSTIN STATE UNIVERSITY
NACOGDOCHES, TEXAS

# Contents

## PART III

### A SAMPLE DEMONSTRATION

# I.S.Q.D.
## Identification System for Questioned Documents

# PART I
# DISCOVERY OF THE FACT

# Handwriting Reduced to Strokes

T HERE IS NO REASON WHY any questioned document cannot undergo a scientific test much the same as any other laboratory test.

*Graphoanalysis,* the science on which this identification system is based, breaks down handwriting into two fundamental strokes — the straight stroke and the curve — and the direction in which they are written. No letters or words, as such, are considered. Only the strokes, wherever they may occur, and in whatever formation they may appear, are weighed in their relationship to the other strokes in the writing.

It is through the combination of two or more of these fundamental strokes that writing is constructed. Two curves, for example, can be put together in one way to form what is known as a loop, or they can put together in another way to form what is known as a circle.

# Method: Twelve Points of Comparison

T HE FIRST STEP IN ANY LEGAL handwriting examination is to observe the general appearance of the questioned writing as compared with the genuine standard writing. By this method the conspicuous characteristics are determined. It is in the breakdown of handwriting stroke by stroke that the inconspicuous characteristics are detected.

The following method of making a scientific comparison, stroke by stroke, of a questioned writing with the genuine, places handwriting identification on the same basis as fingerprint identification. No matter in which laboratory the test is made, or by which trained technician it is made, the conclusion will hold true.

### POINT 1: UNIFORMITY

Does the questioned writing have a smooth, rhythmic, free-flowing appearance?

*Are the strokes connected in a smooth, rhythmic manner?*

### POINT 2: IRREGULARITIES

Does the questioned writing appear awkward, ill-formed, messy, and slowly drawn, giving the look of a general lack of harmony indicating unnaturalness?

*Are the strokes patched, retouched?*

*Penrod and Sam*

*Are there small marks near the strokes?*

*Penrod and Sam*

*Are the strokes wavering?*

*Penrod and Sam*

*Are the connecting strokes broken?*

*Are the circle formations made up of separate strokes?*

*Sam*

*Are there pen lifts?*

*Penrod and*

*Are there vertical strokes mixed with a forward slant? (See Section 6.)*

*foodie*

*Look for individualized strokes (not a sign of forgery) for identification.*

## POINT 3: SIZE AND PROPORTION

Habit impels us to write in the same relative proportion. A precision ruler should be used to measure the height of the overall writing, as well as the height of individual strokes, in proportion to each other.

*What is the height of the overall writing?*

*What is the height of the short letters in relationship to the tall ones?*

*Do the strokes diminish in size?*

*Do they increase in size?*

*Are they narrow in proportion as they are tall?*

*Are the strokes above and below the line balanced?*

*How tall are the d and t stems in proportion to the rest of the writing?*

*Are the strokes ill-formed?*

## POINT 4: ALIGNMENT

The exemplar of handwriting should next be checked for its alignment with either a ruled line upon which it is written, or an imaginary baseline. Irregularities in alignment may be imperceptible until measured systematically with a precision ruler.

*Do the strokes follow straight along the baseline?*

*Do the letter strokes leave the baseline?*

*Do the word strokes leave the baseline?*

*Do the sentence formations create a convex or concave baseline?*

*Do the sentence formations consistently run uphill?*

*Consistently run downhill?*

*Or form converging "railroad track?"*

### POINT 5: SPACING

A careful observation of the general spacing of the writing on a page should be made, and the width of margins determined. Paragraph indentations should be measured, as well as both the space between lines and the space between individual stroke formations.

⟵*It is my habit
to start my para-
graphs this far a-
way from the mar-
gin.*

*Is the left margin essentially even?*

⇢*It is my habit
to start my para-
graphs this far
away from the
margin.*

*Is it jagged?*

*It is my habit
to start my
paragraphs
this far
from the
margin.*

*It is my habit
to start my
paragraphs
this far
from the
margin.*

*Do the strokes hit the margin at an oblique angle?*

*Sam    Sam    S' am*

*How much space is there between capitals and small letters?*

*P.S.*    *P.S.*    *P. S*

*Between separate capitals?*

*Penrod ↓ and ↓ Sam*

*Penrod and Sam*

*Between word formations?*

*Penrod Sam*

*In connecting strokes?*

*Penrod Sam*

*Proportion of space breaks between letters*

## POINT 6: DEGREE OF SLANT

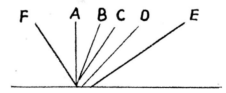

An inexpensive, transparent plastic chart formerly used by Graphoanalysts for measuring the slant of a hand     ıg is particularly suitable for the measuring of slant ir.     es-tioned document work.

The chart was designed after years of research, and is more expedient in determining the slant of a handwriting than adapting ordinary measuring devices, such as a 90 degree protractor, to the upstrokes of a handwriting.

A chart can be made by placing a small piece of heavy plastic or glass over the illustration shown above, and tracing it with India ink.

In the use of the chart, only the upstrokes of a handwriting are measured. A forger who attempts to disguise his writing by changing the slant may be successful in maintaining the disguised slant in the predominant upstrokes, but will have a difficult time in controlling the less dominant strokes of the lower case letters.

A systematic comparison of the slant of the questioned writing should be made with that of the genuine writing. It is to be noted that a handwriting may not necessarily have a consistent slant. In this case, which is known as a variable slant, the forged writing can be just as easily detected by the proportion of variable strokes in each of the exemplars.

### POINT 7: WEIGHT OF STROKES

Strokes in a handwriting may consist of very fine lines, medium, or thick lines. Any straight edge ruler designed for precision measurement may be used to gauge the width of a stroke. Again, a variable width may be encountered, but this, too, will give away the forger when the two handwritings are compared by the proportion of the variable widths of strokes.

### POINT 8: T-BARS AND I-DOTS

One of the most telltale strokes which will give away the forger is the *t*-crossing; another is the *i*-dot. No matter how careful the imitator may be, he will have a hard time not leaving his own characteristics behind in making these strokes.

In the mechanical comparison between a purported forged writing and the genuine, the following earmarks should be determined in regard to the crossbar, in relation to the rest of the strokes in the writing:

*Is it light in weight?*

*Is it heavy in weight?*

*Is it short in relationship to the stem?*

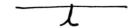

*Is it long in relationship to the stem?*

*Where is it located on the stem?*

*Is it on the left of the stem?*

*Is it on the right of the stem?*

*Is it convex?*

*Is it concave?*

*Does it fade?*

*Remain constant?*

*Grow heavier?*

*Does it slant toward the baseline?*

*Does it slant away from the baseline?*

*Does it have an initial hook?*

*Does it have a terminal hook?*

*Is the stem uncrossed?*

*Is it tied?*

Similar observations should be noted in regard to the *i*-dots (and *j*-dots).

*Is it light?*

*Is it firm?*

*Where is it located above the stem?*

*Is it on the left of the stem?*

*Is it on the right of the stem?*

*Is it a small circle made clockwise?*

*Is it a small circle made counterclockwise?*

*Is it a jab?*

*Is the dot missing?*

*Note:* Since a combination of more than one type of the above illustrated strokes is commonly found in any one handwriting, a mathematical count of each type of stroke must be made before a comparison can be undertaken.

## POINT 9: THE NEEDLE, THE WEDGE, THE ROUND, THE FLAT

A handwriting should be examined to determine if it is primarily composed of sharp, needle-like strokes; wedge-shaped strokes; rounded strokes; flattop strokes; or a combination of two or more of these types of strokes.

A careful examination of the strokes which form the *m*'s, *n*'s, and *r*'s in any one handwriting will disclose a consistent formation of one or more of the above types. In a case where more than one type of formation is used, the proportion will be constant and can be measured mathematically.

*The needle*

*The wedge*

*The rounded or curved*

*The flattop or square*

*m   m   n   n   u   l*

*A combination of the above*

*Note:* It is to be remembered that these formations of strokes may occur *anywhere* in a given handwriting, e.g. in the formation of strokes which we call an *h*, and *s*, or inverted and below the line in the *p*. It is only for the purpose of communication that the combination of strokes are called by their letter names.

### POINT 10: LOOPS

Curved strokes, combined to form what is known as a loop, may occur below the baseline of the writing, or above the baseline. These are checked in relation to the rest of the writing for the following:

*long*

*Are they long?*

*little   going*

*Are they short?*

*long*

*Are they broad?*

*little going*

*Are they narrow?*

*little*

*Are they needle-like?*

*little*

*Wedge-shaped?*

*little*

*Rounded?*

*little going*

*Flat or squared off?*

*long you*
*long lungs*

*Do the loops of one line run into the lines above or below it?*

*Do the loops start above the baseline?*

*Are there loops where they do not occur in the copy book?*

*Are the loops made clockwise or counterclockwise?*

*Are the loops unfinished?*

*Tied around a stem?*

*Is there an initial loop within a circle formation?*

*Is there a final loop within a circle formation?*

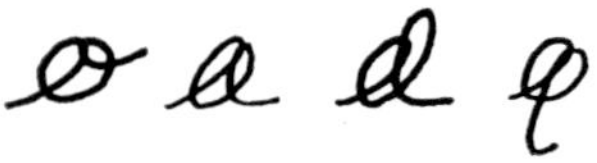

*Are there double loops within a circle formation?*

### Absence of Loops

Handwriting should be checked for the characteristic of making straight strokes in the place of where loops would ordinarily occur in the copy book.

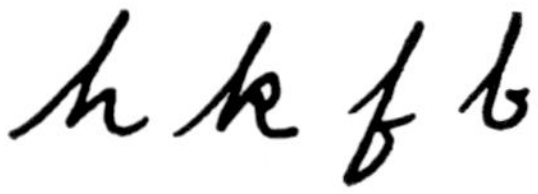

*Above the line*

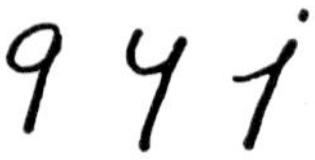

*Below the line*

### POINT 11: CIRCLE FORMATIONS

A single curved line occurring at the baseline is known as a circle formation.

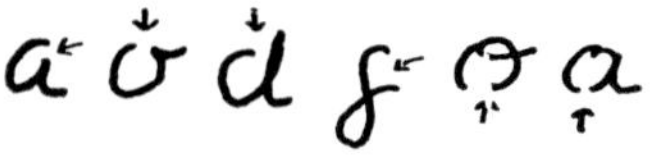

*Are the circle formations open?*

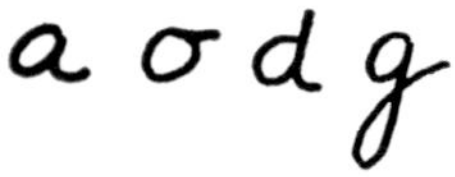

*Closed?*

*a o d a*

*Are they broad?*

*a o d i*

*Narrow?*

*a o d i*

*Filled in with ink?*

## POINT 12: INITIAL AND FINAL STROKES

Perhaps the most inconspicuous characteristics, and those the most difficult for the forger to duplicate, are found in the initial and final strokes of a handwriting. A systematic comparison of each of these strokes will give the examiner revealing evidence.

### Initial Strokes

*chr im m*

*Do the initial strokes begin with a large hook, a fishhook, or an almost imperceptible hook?*

*Cm Mh*

*With a flourish? Flat or squared off?*

*m b t*

*With an inflexible upstroke from the baseline?*

*m b t*

*With a flexible upstroke from the baseline?*

*love her*

*Start part way up the staff?*

*tom boy*

*Start below the baseline?*

*to be me*

*With a simple, direct downstroke?*

*l u t*

*With a "running start?"*

*t b m*

*Heavy in proportion to the rest of the strokes?*

*t b m*

*Light in proportion to the rest of the strokes?*

**Final Strokes**

*s t m u y*

*Do the final strokes end wih a large hook, a fishhook, or an almost imperceptible hook?*

*m y B*

*With a flourish?*

*t r l*

*Abruptly at the baseline?*

*t r l*

*With a flexible forward stroke?*

*r s m*

*With an inflexible forward stroke?*

*s s D*

*Above the baseline?*

*Below the baseline?*

*Do they fade?*

*Grow heavier?*

*End in a blob?*

*Are they patched?*

*Section 3*

# Conclusion

T HE PRINCIPLE UNDERLYING the identification of a handwriting is the same as that of any other thing which has a
great number of possible variations. The identity or difference is made by a systematic comparison of all the elements
(in handwriting, the strokes) which all together make up
the conclusion. It is the *combination* of measurments and
characteristics that help to identify a handwriting — a combination mathematically beyond mere chance.

There are so many possible combinations of strokes that
it would be impossible to discuss all of them here. But it is to
be remembered that *all* strokes are to be handled in the same
manner — whether the strokes appear in a printed writing,
a combination of printing and cursive writing, or in strike-
outs.

*Section 4*

# Summary

Summed up, there are twelve points of comparison in handwriting identification just as there are twelve points of comparison in fingerprint identification.

1. Uniformity
2. Irregularities
3. Size and proportion
4. Alignment
5. Spacing
6. Degree of slant
7. Weight of strokes
8. *t*-bars and *i*-dots
9. The needle, the wedge, the round, the flat
10. Loops
11. Circle formations
12. Initial and final strokes.

# PART II
# PROOF OF THE FACT

*Section 1*

# Reasons and Basis for Opinion

It is of little benefit to discover the fact that a questioned document is a forgery, or that it is genuine, if the fact is not presented in court in such a manner that the judge and jury will also reach the correct conclusion.

When the document examiner has reached his finding as to whether a specimen is forged or genuine, he must prepare his reasons and basis for opinion in a way that they can be demonstrated to others. The value of his opinion as evidence depends upon the clarity with which he demonstrates its correctness.

*Section 2*

# The Purpose and Value of Photographs

T HE BEST WAY to demonstrate the reasons and basis for opinion is by photographs. Photographs appeal to the sense of sight. By presenting good, clear prints, the twelve points of comparison presented in Part I of this manual will silently reach the minds of those to be convinced.

Photographs are a means of *reporting*. The purpose of presenting photographs in a questioned document case in court is to report to the judge and jury the facts discovered by the handwriting examiner.

Photography means *writing with light*. A good, clear picture of the twelve points of comparison, drawn with rays of light by a camera, will tell a story. It will interpret the original specimen of writing. In addition, it will interpret each point which it reveals with complete impartiality.

The words of an examiner may be tinctured with prejudice, but photographs are entirely *objective*. The camera lens records a writing accurately and with precision. Photography lifts document testimony out of the realm of opinion and its pitfalls, and places it on a demonstrative basis. Opinion testimony speaks to the observer's belief; visible testimony speaks to his intelligence. The objective photograph represents far better evidence than the most detailed description.

Another reason for photographing a document is that a photograph is *permanent*. If the judge and jury must take turns viewing the specimens under a microscope, each observer has but a fleeting picture in his mind of the points in question. Not only is the use of a microscope time consuming, when twelve points of comparison are to be considered, but the observers cannot all see the points at the same time while the examiner is commenting on them.

Unlike the original document, photographs may be enlarged to reveal characteristics which otherwise might remain hidden. Also, photographs may be cut up into parts so that the characteristics can be classified. These purposes, together with the use of photographs in cases where the question regards the continuity of strokes, or retouching, will be discussed in subsequent sections.

In court when photographs are admitted in evidence, their value alone may be enough to prove the facts at issue as against the testimony of witnesses on the other side.

# Forensic Photography

F ORENSIC, OR DOCUMENT, photography is no do-it-yourself job. It requires specific knowledge, skill in techniques, and special equipment.

The handwriting examiner who plays amateur photographer to save the cost of hiring a document photographer, will pay for it in unsatisfactory exhibits for his demonstration in court. The exhibits may even be declared inadmissible as evidence.

Using I.S.Q.D., an analyst may have a foolproof case to report with his twelve points of comparison; but faulty negatives, made on the wrong type of film, inferior developing techniques, or fuzzy enlargements, will make the results useless.

Even an expert commercial portrait photographer may not be equipped with the necessary apparatus to photograph documents. Special lenses and other equipment are essential to make a detailed photograph showing very distinctly each of the twelve points of comparison. They must be bright enough, yet not glaring, so that the judge and jury can see them easily as the examiner directs their attention to them.

The forensic photographer will determine accurately the volume and angle of lighting required to obtain a photograph of the true weight of the strokes of the writing. (See *Weight of Strokes,* Part I, Sec. 2.) The photograph must reveal the graduated depth of the pen lines and the pressure and rhythm of the writing.

A true photograph, i.e. a perfect document photograph, will tell its own story to the judge and jury.

# Enlargements of Twelve Points of Comparison

W HEN THE HANDWRITING ANALYST has sifted out his twelve points of comparison, and has determined that the writing is a forgery, or is genuine, he must put his findings into a form that will aid those who are to be convinced to reach the same conclusion.

Oral testimony is ineffective because members of the jury are usually unfamiliar with handwriting analysis. The testimony must be presented in a form in which the juror can see it for himself.

In most cases, handwriting in its natural size is too small to use for an analytical study by the untrained eye. An accurately enlarged photograph is indispensable to report and interpret the investigator's findings. Enlargements enable the judge and jury to follow the technical report of the handwriting expert as he is giving it.

The handwriting should be enlarged four times its natural size. This will make the specimen four times as distinct as it was originally. Too great an enlargement will distort the writing, lose the detail, and may conceal just the evidence the examiner is trying to lay bare.

Along with the enlargement, however, the handwriting analyst should also display, for comparison, a photograph of the handwriting in its natural size. When the analyst points out a minute characteristic in the enlargement — which the untrained eye did not detect in the natural size — then returns to the handwriting in its natural size, the untrained eye will be able to see that particular characteristic there which it hadn't seen at first.

The most important function of enlargements is to make conspicuous the inconspicuous characteristics found in the scientific breakdown of a writing.

*Uniformity.* In its natural size, the handwriting may appear to be smooth and free-flowing, but the enlarged photograph will reveal hesitation with corrugations, i.e. wavelike ridges in the strokes. These are caused when a writing has been slowly drawn, a sign of forgery.

*Irregularities.* Pen lifts, broken connecting strokes, and small marks made near the strokes, almost imperceptible in a writing in its natural size, will appear with surprising clearness in an enlargement.

*Size and Proportion.* Measurements of the height of the overall writing, and of the individual strokes in proportion to each other, can be reported to the court and jury more easily from an enlargement of the handwriting.

*Alignment.* Irregularities in the alignment of a handwriting may not be apparent until measured with a precision ruler. As in the matter of the size and proportion of the writing, measuring, and reporting, the alignment can be done more easily from an enlarged photograph.

*Spacing.* An enlarged photograph will reveal with remarkable clarity the amount of space between capitals and small letters, between separate capital letters, and between word formations. It will reveal the amount of space between connecting strokes, and the proportion of space breaks between the letters.

*Degree of Slant.* Although the slant of the predominant upstrokes of a writing may be conspicuous in the specimen's natural size, the degree of slant of the less dominant strokes of the lower case letters may be obscure. Since a forger who attempts to disguise his writing by changing the slant will almost invariably have difficulty in maintaining the disguise while forming the less dominant strokes, the measurement of the slant of the lower case letters becomes important. This measurement can be shown very effectively in an enlarged photograph, where the difference or similarity in slant is more easily noticed.

*Weight of Strokes.* The width of the strokes composing the specimen can be more easily gauged and reported to the court and jury from an enlargement of the handwriting. When the proportions of the writing are enlarged, even the faintest strokes which otherwise would escape observation will be exposed.

*t-Bars and i-Dots.* An enlarged photograph brings to attention and observation some of the indiscernible characteristics of these telltale strokes. For example, it will divulge whether a circle *i*-dot was made clockwise or counterclockwise. Such peculiarities often become paramount factors in establishing whether the writing is genuine or forged.

*The Needle, the Wedge, the Round, the Flat.* Sharp, needle-like strokes, wedge-shaped strokes, rounded and flattop strokes will appear with striking distinctness in an enlarged photograph. A forgery of these formations may be a good simulation in resemblance of the genuine, but the photograph will show that a clear and actual difference does exist.

*Loops.* Individual characteristics and peculiarities in the formation of the loops in a handwriting are made evident when they are enlarged. Loops eclipsed within a circle formation, for instance, will be uncovered in the enlargement.

*Initial and Final Strokes.* An enlargement will disclose hooks at the beginnings and endings of strokes which were invisible to the naked eye when viewed in the natural size of the writing. It will give away the flexibility of initial and final strokes, their weight and patching.

*Enlargements in General.* The microscope or magnifying glass discovers the twelve points of comparison, but the enlarged photograph displays them to the observers for their decision. Unlike an oral witness giving his opinion, an enlarged photograph is a witness of facts which cannot be disputed. Without error, the camera lens never fails to record all the significant characteristics of a handwriting. In court, an enlarged photograph is sometimes absolutely conclusive as evidence.

# Duplicate Photographs

ENOUGH PHOTOGRAPHS MUST be reproduced to provide each observer with a set of perfect copies of the questioned and standard writings which the examiner will be demonstrating in court. This means that every juror, as well as the judge and the attorneys on both sides of the case, should be provided with duplicate photographs.

Including the set for the examiner himself, sixteen sets of photographs will be furnished. The examiner is warned not to economize in this proceeding. A case that may involve thousands of dollars might be jeopardized, or even lost, for lack of a sufficient number of duplicate photographs.

Individual exhibits will give those who are to decide the matter unlimited opportunity to make a careful study and comparison of the points at issue. They furnish the observers a means of following the technical testimony as it is being given.

Although there are various projectors on the market that reproduce handwriting thrown onto a screen, they are not recommended for use in a questioned document case in court. An individual photograph that the observer can hold in his hands at a normal reading level is more effective. It affords him close observation, and enables him to scrutinize each of the twelve points of comparison.

## Section 6

# Photomicrographs

Photomicrographs are an improvement of the usual enlarged photograph, because in the process of enlargement many of the characteristics are minimized.

The photomicrograph is a direct enlargement of the specimen in a single operation. The characteristics that are indistinguishable by direct observation are magnified in the operation and reproduced as they were seen under the microscope.

In this type of reproduction, direct enlargements are made so as to show characteristics which are of a microscopic nature. This is done by replacing the eyepiece of a microscope with a camera. Color filters are used to emphasize the specific characteristics of the writing which the examiner wants to expose. Ultraviolet light may be used to bring out otherwise invisible details.

Photomicrographs are the best evidence in showing detail. When it is necessary to demonstrate some point of comparison or a particular characteristic in exact detail, which is not distinct in the usual enlarged photograph, that point should be photographed with a microscope and camera.

Photomicrographs are helpful in cases where it is particularly desirable to show the weight of the strokes, or their corregation; in cases regarding patching; where the handwriting expert needs to bring out clearly the very faintest of strokes or marks; and in issues involving any third dimension characteristics.

As in any document photography, photomicrographs should be made by an experienced document photographer. Correctly made, these scientific pictures produced through a microscope can be convincing evidence to the eyes of judge and jury.

*Section 7*

# Transmitted Light

W HEN THE EXAMINER desires to illustrate a point of comparison that is not visible on its surface, it can be shown clearly to the observer by a *transmitted light* photograph.

Whereas photographs made by direct light show all that can be seen on the face of the handwriting, they do not show what lies beneath the surface. A very skillfully made signature may show no signs of pen lifts, for example, or of patching when examined on its surface by direct light; but these irregularities will show up clearly when they are subjected to transmitted light.

This type of photograph is made by placing a light bulb behind the specimen so that the light will pass through the paper and portray all the factors of the writing at different degrees of density.

Transmitted light is particularly useful where the question is one of continuity of strokes or of patching. In the case of continuity of strokes, transmitted light will show the even distribution of ink in strokes connected in a smooth, rhythmic manner, or the uneven distribution of ink in pen lifts (stops at unusual places) .

In a retouched (patched) writing, it will show the existence of the added ink used in the retouching. When viewed by direct light, the added ink in a patching may not be noticed, but the difference in opaqueness at a particular point will show up plainly in a photograph made by transmitted light.

In certain cases regarding initial and final strokes, where the distribution of ink is of importance, the use of transmitted light photographs will show the degrees of density.

Final strokes that end in blobs, for example, will be brought out clearly by transmitted light.

The order in which crossed strokes were made can also be demonstrated by this type of photograph.

Photographs made with transmitted light should be accurately enlarged and displayed as identification evidence in court. They are almost self-explanatory, and will prove to be valuable testimony.

## Section 8

# Transparent Photographs

It is a well known fact that no one writes his signature exactly the same way twice. He cannot produce two signatures alike in every minute detail. When two signatures show suspicious similarity, they should be held up to the light with one signature placed directly over the other. If they match precisely at every point, one or both of the signatures has been traced either by hand or mechanically with a copying contrivance.

When the handwriting examiner has determined that a signature is a tracing, he should have a qualified document photographer make a transparent photograph for the examiner's demonstration in court.

A transparent photograph, or *translite,* is a picture on film made visible by light shining through from behind. The photographer makes a positive print of the questioned signature on translite film, which is a special type of translucent film that resembles frosted glass. When this print is placed directly over an ordinary photograph of the specimen, both will be in the same position at every point and emerge as one clear-cut signature. Enlargements should be made of the transparencies for the demonstration in court.

The demonstration of superimposing the signatures does not necessitate holding the transparencies up to a window, or an artificial light, as was necessary in the days when two ordinary positive films were used. By holding both photographs in their hands and simply placing the translite directly over the regular print, the judge and jury can observe that all parts of the two signatures match exactly at every point, giving the appearance of a single signature.

Translites are also useful in demonstrating that a questioned signature is genuine. Side by side, two signatures may closely resemble each other but, when superimposed, they do not match perfectly. The examiner can then point out the differences, and prove that the signature which was alleged to be a traced forgery is in fact genuine.

Transparent photographs can be valuable in assisting the judge and jury to decide if a questioned signature is a tracing or if it is genuine. When relevant to the case they should be included in the individual sets of photographs for each observer.

## Section 9

# Markings on Photographs

ALL PHOTOGRAPHS INTRODUCED in court as evidence by a handwriting examiner should be free of all markings of any kind.

Numbers, letters, arrows, or any other marks for purposes of identification will deface the photograph. Underlining, or marking a photograph on its face with initials or dates is to be avoided. Pencil or ink marks tend to confuse the observer. Even if they don't come in contact with the handwriting in question, a photograph so marked will lose its character as a photograph and depreciate in value.

The examiner must not mark a photograph by retouching it in any way. Retouching constitutes an alteration, and may mislead the observers as well as destroy the testimony altogether.

When the examiner wants to show the twelve points of comparison graphically with small arrows, or number them, he can mark a duplicate photograph which can be used as a chart, or offered in evidence for identification only. (See Part II, Sec. 13.)

In issues where size and proportion, or the degree of slant, are essential points of comparison, the specimen should be photographed with a measuring device. This is done by photographing the questioned writing and the standards with a superimposed transparent plastic ruler, or the plastic chart shown in Part I, Section 2, Point 6.

This method does not constitute marking, and does not destroy the admissibility of the photograph as evidence. However, the exihibit will be marked "for identification," and accepted in evidence for identification only. The photograph representing the original writing cannot be marked in any way.

Generally, signatures are photographed with a metric ruler placed beneath the signatures on the face of the specimen; this is perfectly acceptable in evidence for identification. Although it has been said that a decimal ruler should be used because it is better understood by a lay jury, the metric system is in more general use throughout the world and should be used in questioned document cases. It is also handier because photography equipment is geared to the metric system.

A photograph is self-explanatory. It illustrates an idea in a clear, graphic way, and should contain no markings which are not part of the photograph, or of the original writing which it represents.

This rule does not, of course, include the handwriting examiner's markings on the backs of the photographs. Every specimen taken into court should carry the handwritng analyst's mark of identification, for example, his initials.

At times the opposing attorney may attempt to confuse or trap the witness by handing him, and questioning him about, similar photographs which are not those the witness had previously examined. By looking on the back for his mark of identification, the examiner can be sure whether or not a photograph is actually one he has studied.

*Section 10*

# Photostatic Photographs

T HERE ARE MANY TYPES of photographic copying machines on the market today. Photographs made by photographic copying, such as those made by xerography or a Photostat® machine, are not suitable for questioned document illustrations.

In this type of photograph, some of the most important characteristics and significant evidences of forgery are concealed. Much detail is lost. One of the most suspicious signs of forgery is a slowly drawn handwriting with the resulting wavelike ridges in its strokes. This evidence does not appear in a photograph unless the characteristic of the line quality is plainly shown. The line quality is not clearly shown in photostatic photographs which smooth out these corregated strokes, making them appear uniform.

In a photostatic photograph, the weight of the strokes is indistinguishable. Fine strokes and heavy strokes look alike, covering up evidence which the examiner wishes to reveal. Every stroke of the original writing is shown in one flat shade without any degree of depth.

Intricate characteristics in the formation of *t*-bars, *i*-dots and the needle, wedge, round, and flat strokes do not reproduce accurately in a Photostat. Irregularities such as patched strokes are hidden. Minute characteristics like those found in various circle formations, and in initial and final strokes, are also hidden in the process of photostating in which sensitive paper is used instead of film.

When only the subject matter of a document — deeds, birth certificates, military discharges — is wanted for record, a photostatic photograph is sufficient. It is not satisfactory as a questioned document illustration.

# Mounting Exhibits

THE DUPLICATE PHOTOGRAPHS that are to be used by the judge, jury, and opposing attorneys should be of a size that can be conveniently handled, yet will portray clearly the twelve points of comparison that are being considered. They should not be a size larger than can be seen all at once at the usual reading distance. A standard 11 by 14 inch photograph is adequate for these purposes.

Again, the demonstrator is warned not to try to economize. If he furnishes the observers with small 5 by 7 inch skimpy prints, even though they may illustrate the points he has indicated on his demonstration chart, the photographs may seem trivial and be set aside. On the other hand, 11 by 14 inch photographs, properly mounted and placed in the hands of an observer, are not so easily ignored.

The document photographer will see that the prints are properly mounted so as to take up the least amount of space, and that they will lie flat and not buckle.

There should be enough border in the mounting to allow for any identification the examiner wishes to indicate on the exhibit. As it was pointed out in Section 9, the photographs themselves, should not be marked in any way.

The exhibits are numbered in regular order on the border of the mounting, for instance, Q-1, Q-2, Q-3, for the questioned writing; S-1, S-2, S-3, for the standards of comparison. If a date is essential to a specimen, it can be printed inconspicuously on the border of the mounting in such a way as not to interfere with the handwriting at issue.

All exhibits should be marked and arranged in advance of the court trial in order to save time and confusion. All photographs should be placed *separately* in a folder or heavy envelope, in the order in which each is to be demonstrated, and given to the observer as a complete set so that there will be no unnecessary interruptions during the demonstration.

The set of photographs should not be bound together into a book or album. As attractive and convenient as this may seem, it is not expedient. Separate exhibits afford side by side comparison of the photographs of the questioned writing with those of the standards.

For his demonstration, 20 by 24 inch photographs are recommended as the size for the examiner to use as charts. The more overpowering the display, the more impressed the observers.

# Classification of Twelve Points of Comparison

Most jurors are unfamiliar with handwriting analysis. Their eyes are not trained to carry a characteristic, or point of comparison, from one photograph to another. Even the most conspicuous resemblances or differences in points of comparison may not register in their minds, unless these points can be examined close together.

To accomplish this purpose, photographs of the questioned and of the standard writing are cut apart, and the twelve points of comparison are classified. These parts are placed close together, side by side in parallel columns. In this position, the points that differ will appear to differ more widely, and the points that are alike will appear to resemble each other more closely.

In this method of exhibition, the points of similarity in a genuine writing, and the points of dissimilarity in a forged writing — as compared to the standard writings — can be seen at once by the judge and jury. This instant comparison eliminates the necessity of switching one's eyes from one photograph to another in order to create a mental picture of a point of comparison.

If the observers themselves were to make these photographic groupings, it would be almost impossible for them to retain the images of the characteristics in the process of leaving one photograph and taking up another.

In comparing twelve points of comparison to determine their similarity or dissimilarity, they must be placed side by side in a photograph so that the observer can see the whole group at one time, as the demonstrator points out the characteristics.

In a side by side exhibit, the uniformity or irregularity of the strokes can be easily compared. The size and proportion, the spacing and the weight of the strokes can be measured. Intricate formations of the curved strokes made into circles or loops can be recognized.

Along with the cut-apart photographs, the original photographs are available to the observer in his individual set of exhibits. After he has seen the twelve points of comparison, side by side, he can then compare them with the original photographs of the questioned and of the genuine exemplars.

The classification of the points of comparison, by cutting them apart and placing them side by side in parallel columns, is essential to a complete demonstration in court. An illustration of this type of exhibit can be seen in Figure 10 of the concrete application of I.S.Q.D. in Part III, Section 12.

*Section 13*

# Photographs Admissible as Evidence

In this day of modern cameras, there is no question as to the admissibility of photographs *per se* as evidence in court. Modernized lenses make photographic reproductions absolutely accurate and without distortion, providing they have been made properly by a qualified photographer.

There can be no more objection to an examiner's use of enlarged photographs to illustrate his twelve points of comparison, than to the use of a magnifying glass to demonstrate them. The photograph is merely an enlarged view of the specimen in a permanent form.

However, all photographs must be *proved* to be correct reproductions of the original writings in order to be admissible as evidence. They must be free from all defects and distortion. The slightest imperfection in a photograph will nullify its admission. A faulty photograph actually presents a false representation of the true facts and should never be offered in evidence.

A correct photograph is sharp, and shows distinctly all the necessary details. It illustrates the twelve points of comparison so that they are easily recognized by judge and jury.

As seen in Section 9, no markings of any kind should appear on a photograph. Marks weaken the evidential value of a photograph, and the examiner who inscribes it with any markings whatsoever risks its not being admitted in evidence. He also must not retouch the photograph. Retouching constitutes an alteration and can destroy the testimony as evidence.

### Photostatic Photographs

In the event that the handwriting witness must necessarily resort to a photostatic photograph as an illustration, the Photostat must be proved to be a correct and direct copy of the original specimen before it will be admitted as evidence. It must not be a photostatic copy of a Photostat. When a Photostat is made of a Photostat, a forger can make another document altogether from the original one by altering it and substituting other writing for that which was originally there. Although the first Photostat will reveal the paper connections, they will gradually be eliminated with each subsequent photostatic copy.

It is doubtful that the court will allow the comparison of the characteristics of handwriting from a photostatic photograph, but this is left to the discretion of the trial judge who will decide according to what is to be proved, and according to the circumstances of the case.

### Proving a Photograph

A photograph is proved to be correct by having the photographer who made it testify that he made it, that he is qualified to make such a photograph, and that it is correct. His mark of identification should appear on the back of it.

If the photographer who made the photograph is not available, another qualified photographer may testify. It is not necessary that the negative be developed by the photographer who proves the photograph, or that the print be made by him. He can compare the negative with the original specimen and testify that it is an accurate reproduction of it; and he can examine the print and testify that it is an accurate copy of the negative.

Photographs are often admitted on the testimony of one who hasn't made them. All that is necessary is that they be shown to be accurate reproductions of the original writing.

Even composite photographs, for the purpose of comparison — as in the classification of the twelve points of comparison — are admissible as evidence. However, these will be marked "for identification" by an officer of the court at the time they are admitted. The examiner, or the forensic photographer who made them, will have previously testified as to their authenticity.

Should there ever be any doubt about the accuracy of a photograph, it can easily be proven by comparing it with the original specimen.

*Section 14*

# I.S.Q.D. Admissible as Evidence

I.s.q.d. WITH ITS TWELVE POINTS of comparison, has been accepted in court as a basis for proving that a handwriting is a forgery or is genuine.

In *The Marine Corps v. Gray,* Honolulu, Hawaii, 1969 (a court martial case), the handwriting analyst, who was called in to examine the document in question, used the I.S.Q.D. method of identification to prove the document genuine. The testimony was admitted as evidence, without challenge, and the document was found by the court to be genuine.

Following this case, internationally known Graphoanalyst Doris M. Williamson was retained to investigate another questioned document. The matter was settled out of court. According to the attorney for the case, when the opposing attorney was informed that the identification had been made by the I.S.Q.D. system, he threw in the towel.

Although these are cases in which I.S.Q.D. itself was used, numerous questioned document cases based on identification by Graphoanalysis have been admitted as evidence in court over the years. In Federal court case 28404, *U.S. v. Webster,* District court of Maryland, February 13, 1969, the testimony of a Graphoanalyst won out over that of an F.B.I. handwriting expert.

# PART III
# A SAMPLE DEMONSTRATION
### (Photography by Marvin C. Bein)

# Problem

A DOCUMENT EXAMINER has been presented with the questioned document shown in Figure 1, and asked to compare the signature on it with the standards shown in Figure 2. He is to determine whether the signature on the document has been forged or if it is genuine.

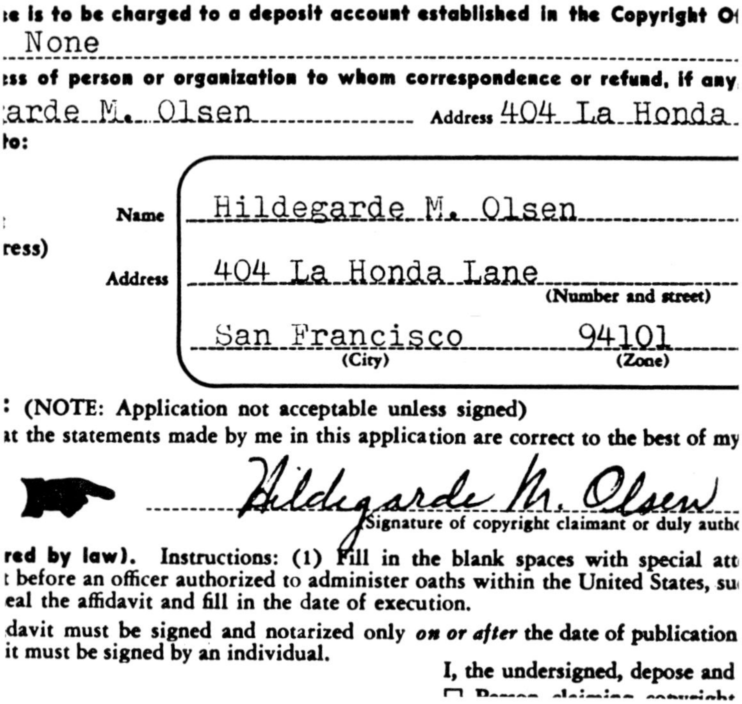

ie is to be charged to a deposit account established in the Copyright O[

  None

iss of person or organization to whom correspondence or refund, if any

arde M. Olsen _____ Address 404 La Honda

to:

| | Name | Hildegarde M. Olsen |
|---|---|---|
| ress) | Address | 404 La Honda Lane |
| | | (Number and street) |
| | | San Francisco          94101 |
| | | (City)                 (Zone) |

: (NOTE: Application not acceptable unless signed)

it the statements made by me in this application are correct to the best of my

*Hildegarde M. Olsen*

Signature of copyright claimant or duly auth(

red by law). Instructions: (1) Fill in the blank spaces with special att
t before an officer authorized to administer oaths within the United States, su:
eal the affidavit and fill in the date of execution.

davit must be signed and notarized only *on or after* the date of publication
it must be signed by an individual.

I, the undersigned, depose and

Figure 1. Questioned signature.

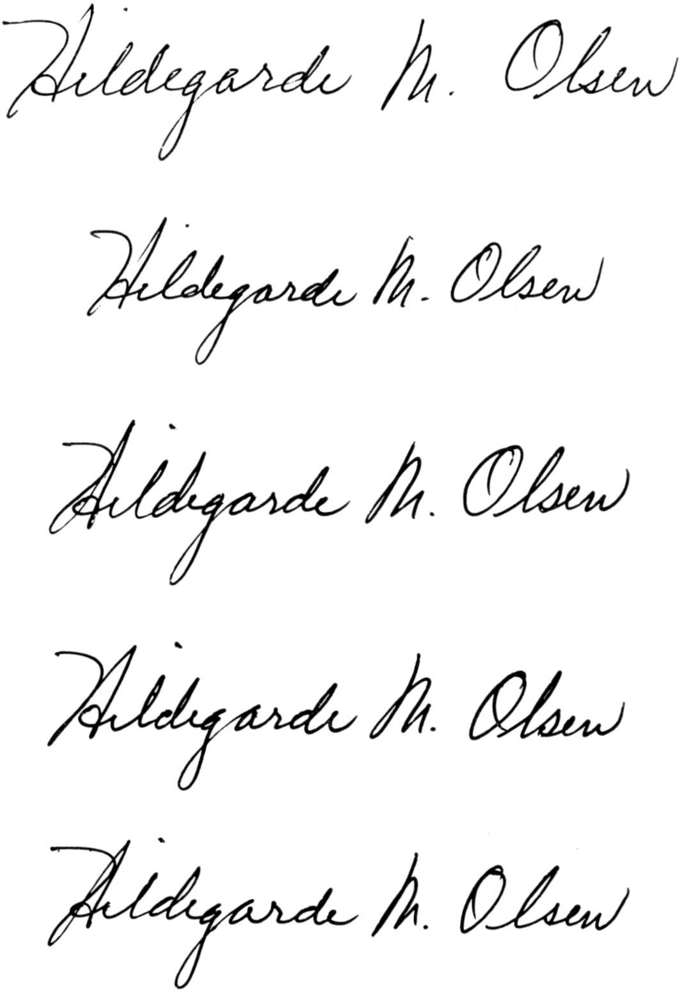

*Figure 2. Standard signatures.*

# Method

U sing I.S.Q.D. — the system set forth in Part I of this manual — as his criterion, the examiner will make a systematic comparison, stroke by stroke, of the questioned signature with the standards. He will look for points of similarity and dissimilarity from which he will later sift out the twelve points of comparison which he will be using as the reasons and basis for his opinion.

### POINT 1: UNIFORMITY

The writing in Figure 1 has a smooth, rhythmic, free-flowing appearance. Note the flexibility of the strokes, especially the spontaneous upstroke of the letter *H*. The strokes are connected in a smooth, rhythmic manner. The writing is *uniform* like that in Figure 2.

### POINT 2: IRREGULARITIES

Does the questioned writing appear awkward, ill-formed, messy, and slowly drawn giving the look of a general lack of harmony indicating unnaturalness? On the contrary, it is clean writing, with the strokes clear-cut and carefully formed.

No small marks are found near the strokes. There are no patched or wavering strokes; the circle formations aren't made up of separate strokes; there are no pen lifts; and the slant of the strokes is uniform.

The connecting strokes are not broken. (Note: connecting strokes are sometimes broken in a natural way, e.g. when the writer stops to dot an *i* or cross a *t*. When the strokes are broken in the manner shown in the illustration of irregularities in Part I, there is a suspicion of forgery.)

The strokes forming the *H* and the *O* in both the questioned and the standard writings are individualized, and these characteristics should be noted as good points of identification to be illustrated later for the demonstration in court.

## POINT 3: SIZE AND PROPORTION

It doesn't take a precision ruler to show that the height of the overall writing in Figure 1 is not the same as that in Figure 2. The height of the questioned writing is less than that in any of the standards. This is dismissed, however, because the questioned signature has been written on a form that limits the height of the overall writing. Note that the length of the questioned signature, itself, is proportionately shorter than that of the standards. (Fig. 3.)

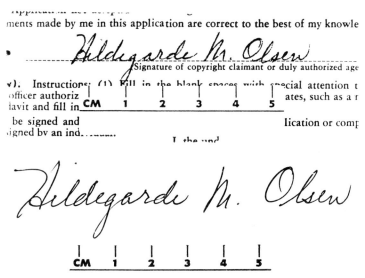

*Figure 3. Signatures with metric scale to show their proportionate lengths.*

To reduce the overall writing in correct proportion, and still maintain the individual characteristics of a writing, is a difficult feat. Measuring the height of the short letters in relationship to the tall ones, it will be found that the writing in Figure 1 is proportionately the same as that in Figure 2.

The strokes in the capital letter *M* diminish in size. This is obvious, and would be obvious to a forger attempting to copy the signature. Not so obvious are the strokes in the last two small letters of *Olsen,* which also diminsh in size, and all the *ga*'s in *Hildegarde* which increase in size. (Fig. 4.)

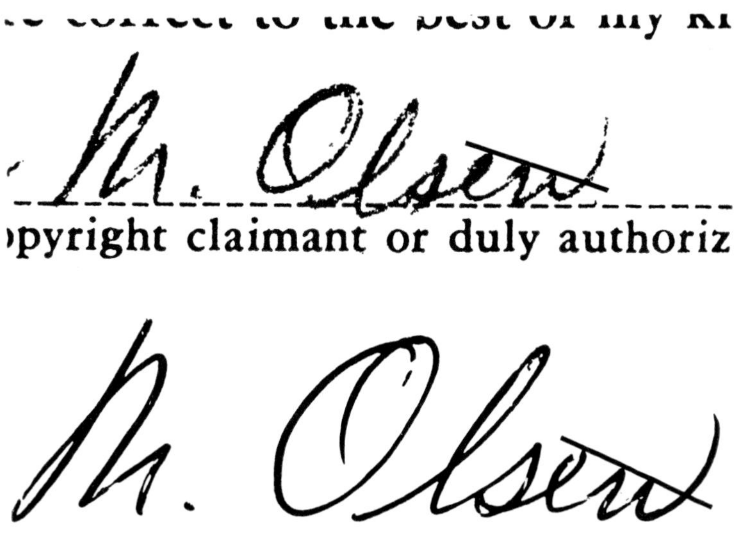

Figure 4. The strokes in the last two small letters of both the questioned and the standard diminish in size.

The strokes are not narrow in proportion as they are tall. They have no cramped appearance. They are spaced by generous connecting strokes. This holds true even in the questioned writing where the freedom of the strokes is limited by the space on the form.

With unique consistency, the length of the strokes of the *g*, below the baseline of the writing, measures the same as the distance between the baseline and the initial stroke of the *H*. This holds true in the questioned writing and in all the standards.

There are no *t*'s in the signatures, but the height of the *d* stems is similar in all the specimens. They are approximately three times the height of the small letters of the signature.

All the strokes are well-formed, although some of them are irregular in proportion because they increase or diminish in size.

### POINT 4: ALIGNMENT

In the questioned writing, the writer had a line to follow. Almost all the upward strokes start from it and return to it. The last five letters of *Hildegarde* and the last three letters of *Olsen* run uphill from the baseline in the questioned writing. There is the suspicion that the writer would consistently write uphill if there were no dotted line to follow.

This is just what is found in all the exemplars of the standard writing. Each signature of the standards runs slightly uphill from the baseline.

The converging "railroad track" formation shown in Part I refers to a document containing several sentences of writing; it does not apply in the case of an isolated signature.

### POINT 5: SPACING

The general spacing of the writing on the page, paragraph indentations, and margins do not apply in this case.

There is no space between the capital *H* and the following small letters in either the questioned writing or in any of the standards; the *H* is joined to the following letter with a connecting stroke.

The space between the final stroke of *Hildegarde* and the capital *M* in the questioned signature is the same (considering proportion) as that in the standard signatures. The same holds true for the space between the capital *M* and the period after it, and between the period and the capital *O* following it, as well as the overall space between the two separate capitals. The capital *O* is separate from the following letters in the word *Olsen,* and the space between them is consistent.

In one of the standards, the spaces will measure greater than those in the other specimens, but they are proportionate within this one signature. The space between the connecting strokes of this particular signature is also greater than that in the other standards, and in the questioned writing, which are proportionately the same.

There are no space breaks between the letters in *Hildegarde* or in *Olsen* in either the questioned or standard writing. All letters in the body of the writing are joined with connecting strokes.

### POINT 6: DEGREE OF SLANT

The slant of genuine signatures varies only to a small extent. If the questioned signature in Figure 1 is genuine, the slant of the upstrokes will correspond consistently with those of the standards in Figure 2.

Using the special slant chart shown in Part I, Section 2, a systematic comparison of the slant of the upstrokes of the signatures shows that the degree of slant of each of those in the questioned writing corresponds consistently with the counterpart strokes in the standards.

Only the upstrokes which start on the baseline are measured. For example, the *l* in *Hildegarde* is the first upstroke measured, because the *i* preceding it begins with an upstroke that does not start from the baseline. The stroke is measured from the point where it leaves the baseline and first turns upward to the point where it stops going up and starts turning down.

## POINT 7: WEIGHT OF STROKES

With the writing instruments generally in use today, the difference in the width of the strokes of a handwriting are not so obvious. Shading is no longer a general factor for the examiner to consider.

However, no matter what writing instrument is used, in a smooth, free-flowing genuine writing the *upstrokes* are consistently *lighter* in weight than the downstrokes. A forger will give himself away by making upstrokes which are the same weight as the downstrokes. This is due to the slowly drawn lines forming a carefully copied writing.

The first upstroke of the *H*, and the upstroke of the lower loop of the *g*, in both the questioned and the standard signatures, are *light* in proportion to the rest of the writing. These similar characteristics can be perceived with the naked eye.

A careful examination under magnification of all the other upstrokes reveals that they also are consistently lighter in weight than the downstrokes. This holds true in both the questioned and the standard signatures, which are constructed throughout with matching strokes of evenly proportionate weight.

## POINT 8: T-BARS AND I-DOTS

Since there are no *t*'s in the signature in question, the examiner will pass over the first part of this section on *t*-bars and go directly to the part regarding *i*-dots for his study and comparison. In his study he will include the period after the capital *M* in each signature.

In a case where there is neither a *t* nor an *i* in a signature, the examiner will disregard Point 8 and select another point of comparison from some other section to substitute for

Point 8. The handwriting analyst will not always be dealing with an ideal case; he must adapt I.S.Q.D. to the particular circumstances of each case he handles.

Even the *i*-dots do not present the examiner with a strong point of comparison in the particular signature at hand. The *i*-dot and the period in the questioned signature resemble some of those in the standards, and are dissimilar to others. The person who wrote the standards does not make a consistent *i*-dot.

However, the weight of the dots is similar, and they are all located high and to the right of the stem. The *i*-dot in the questioned signature is not as far-flung as those in the standards, but the writer was held back somewhat by the limited space. On the other hand, where there was more leeway in making the period after the capital *M,* the dot was placed at the same distance between the two capital letters in all the signatures.

## POINT 9: THE NEEDLE, THE WEDGE, THE ROUND, THE FLAT

Usually a handwriting is composed of a combination of needle, wedge, round, and flat strokes. Where there is a quantity of writing, it is sometimes necessary to count the number of each type of these formations to determine the proportion of each type used in the specimen. This is not necessary when the questioned writing is a signature.

The *r*'s in the questioned signature in Figure 1, and those in the standards in Figure 2, are all flattop. Each of the flat strokes of the *r* commences with a short needle and slants at approximately the same degree.

There is a combination of the round and the wedge in the strokes of the capital *M*. In all the specimens this combination is the same: the first hump of the *M* is rounded, tending toward a wedge, and the second hump is a wedge.

Although the *n* is composed of two wedge strokes, the first stroke is slightly rounded, and the second is a needle-like wedge. This characteristic is also consistent in all the specimens.

### POINT 10: LOOPS

The *l*'s in the signatures in Figures 1 and 2 are long and narrow loops. They are all wedge-shaped tending toward a needle, and they all start from the baseline.

The loops of the *g* in the questioned and the standard signatures are also long, but they are not as narrow as the upper loops, and they are all rounded.

There are two loops in each of the *d* formations where they do not occur in the copy book. The first is an initial loop within the circle formation of the *d*, followed by a loop in the stem of the *d*. Some of these can be seen easily with the naked eye; the other loops, including those in the first *d* in the questioned writing, can be seen under magnification. In addition, all of the *g*'s contain an initial loop within circle formation.

The *H* in each of the specimens has a loop tied around the second stem, and the *s*, in the questioned and in all but one of the standards, has a final loop.

There is also a final loop within the circle formation of the capital *O* in the questioned and standard signatures, although some of them are unfinished loops.

### POINT 11: CIRCLE FORMATIONS

Of the five circle formations found in the questioned signature, which can be made either open or closed, only one — the first *d* in *Hildegarde* — is open. Likewise, the first *d* in all but one of the standards is open. The second *d* in the questioned writing is closed, as well as in four of the five standards.

The *g* and the *a* are closed in the questioned, and variable in the standards. However, of the five *g*'s and the five *a*'s in the standards, the majority of them are closed. All of the capital *O* circle formations are closed.

In general, all the circle formations mentioned above are moderate; they are neither broad nor narrow. Those in the questioned signature are similar in breadth to those in the standard signatures.

The *e*'s, on the other hand, are consistenly narrow. All three of the *e*'s in the questioned writing are filled in with ink, as well as the majority of those in the standards.

## POINT 12: INITIAL AND FINAL STROKES

Initial and final strokes are found in the *body* of a writing as well as at the beginning and end of it. Even though a stroke is connected by a previous or following stroke it still has a beginning and an end. In cases where a clever forger has carefully copied the obvious characteristics of the initial and final strokes of the words in a signature, he may be tripped up by the examiner who has analyzed the initial and final strokes in the body of the writing.

### Initial Strokes

In all of the standards in the case at issue, the initial stroke of the *H* begins with a fishhook. The *H* in the questioned signature begins with an imperceptible hook. The illustration in Figure 1 doesn't show that the form, on which the signature was written, was folded before the signing. The initial stroke started in the fold, and the writing instrument was prevented from making a visible hook.

The initial stroke of the *l* in *Olsen,* in the questioned signature, begins with an impreceptible hook. So do the majority of the *l*'s in the standards.

The *M* in the questioned, and four out of five of the standards, begins with a simple, direct downstroke. The one exception in the standards is another fishhook.

In all of the exemplars — questioned and standards — the *O* begins with a large hook.

The initial strokes in the body of the signature are consistently flexible in both the questioned and the standard writing. The inflexible strokes in the *H, M* and *n* of the questioned writing match the *H, M* and *n* of the standards. Note the initial stroke of the second *d* which is a hook.

All the initial strokes are of the same weight in proportion to each other.

### *Final Strokes*

The final stroke of the last *e* in *Hildegarde* ends above the baseline in both the questioned and the standard signatures.

The final stroke of the *n* in *Olsen* finishes unusually high above the baseline in all the exemplars.

These final strokes of the *e* and the *n* mentioned above all fade.

In all the exemplars the final stroke of the *M* ends abruptly at the baseline.

In the body of the signatures the final strokes fade. Although an occasional final stroke is inflexible, most of them are flexible.

# Sifting Out the Twelve Points
# of Comparison

Guided by the I.S.Q.D. method, the examiner will select the twelve points of comparison which, in his judgment, will most easily reach the eyes and minds of those who are to determine the matter in court.

The twelve points of comparison will usually consist of one characteristic chosen from each of the twelve points set forth in Part I. However, the examiner may have found many more similarities, or dissimilarities, of characteristics than the twelve points of comparison which he has selected. These supplementary characteristics will be held in reserve in case they are needed to ensure the identification.

From the information gathered from studying the questioned and standard signatures in Figures 1 and 2, the examiner has concluded that the questioned signature is *genuine.* To prove his opinion, he might select the similarities in the following twelve points of comparison: (1) the uniformity of the signatures as shown by their free-flowing strokes; (2) the irregularity of the *H;* (3) the *ga's* in *Hildegarde* which increase in proportion; (4) the *garde* letters which align uphill; (5) the spacing between the capitals *M* and *O,* and the period between them; (6) the similarity of slant; (7) the weight of the upstroke of the *g;* (8) the individualized *O,* substituted for the *i*-dot which in this case is not a strong point of comparison; (9) the flat *r;* (10) the long and narrow loops of the *l*'s; (11) the consistently narrow circle formations of the *e*'s; and (12) the final strokes of the *n*'s.

*Section 4*

## Locating a Forensic Photographer

NEXT, A FORENSIC PHOTOGRAPHER will be needed to make the illustrations for the demonstration in court. If he does not already know one, the questioned document examiner can usually find the name of a document photographer in his area by checking the yellow pages of the telephone book.

The examiner may also inquire at his local police department, or county crime lab, if there is a *scientific identification technician* available. These technicians are especially prepared to make photographs in relation to questioned documents.

# Enlargements of Twelve Points
# of Comparison

THE FORENSIC PHOTOGRAPHER will photograph the questioned and standard signatures in their natural size. He will also make enlargements of the questioned and standard signatures four times their natural size.

It is not possible to illustrate the entire enlarged photograph of the questioned signature shown in Figure 5 because of the size of the pages of this manual. However, the portion shown can be compared with that portion of the full signature above it, which will give the reader a good idea of how an enlargement will emphasize the characteristics which the examiner wishes to point out.

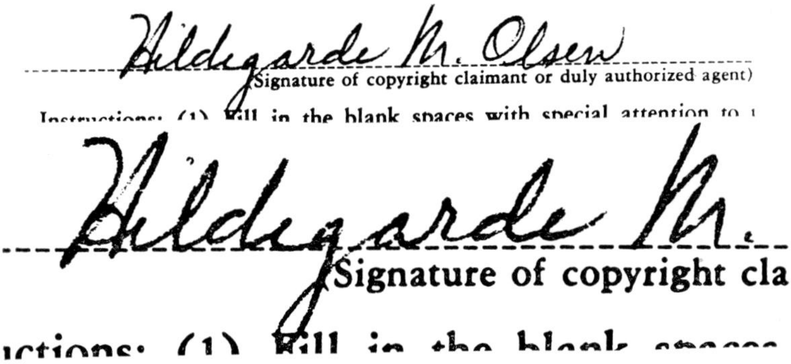

*Figure 5. An enlarged portion of the questioned signature with the same signature, in its entirety, above it in its natural size.*

*Section 6*

# Duplicate Photographs

T HE PHOTOGRAPHER WILL MAKE enough 11 by 14 inch duplicates of the questioned and standard signatures in their natural size, and their enlargements, to furnish the judge, the opposing attorneys and each member of the jury with a set of them, besides those the handwriting examiner will need for himself.

The examiner will need enough extra photographs to cut out from the questioned and standard signatures the twelve points of comparison which he has selected for the identification. These he will arrange side by side in parallel colums as shown in Figure 10 in Section 12. This composite photograph will be included in the set for each observer.

# Photomicrographs

A PHOTOMICROGRAPH OF THE *H* in *Hildegarde* would be the best evidence to show the fishhook on its initial stroke. This type of photograph will also bring out even more clearly than the enlargement the spontaneous upstroke of the *H* which is rather faint in some of the specimens.

Unles the examiner feels that it is important to the case (e.g. if a vital characteristic cannot be detected at all by the observer from an enlargement), it is not necessary to include the photomicrograph in the photograph sets for each observer. In this case, the photomicrograph shown in Figure 6 will be used only as a chart in the court room demonstration.

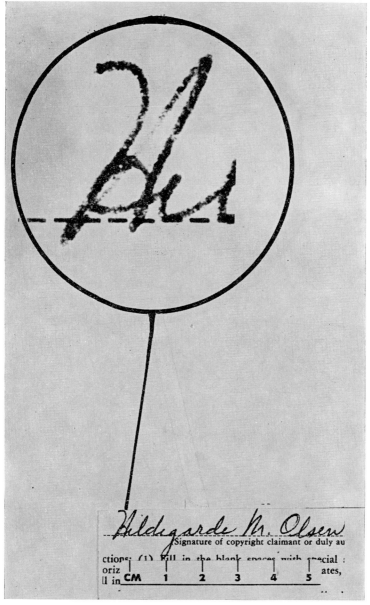

*Figure 6. A photomicrograph showing in detail the aborted fishhook on the initial stroke of the H.*

*Section 8*

# Transmitted Light

I<small>N THE CASE AT HAND,</small> there is such an abundance of similarities of characteristics that the examiner knows that the questioned document is either genuine, or else he is coping with an especially artful forger. In order to be sure, he will want the forensic photographer to make a transmitted light photograph of the questioned writing.

If there was any skillful retouching done, the transmitted light photograph will reveal the added ink used in doing it. Otherwise, this type of photograph will show the even distribution of ink in the strokes, emphasizing their continuity and connection in a smooth, rhythmic manner.

This evidence will strengthen Point 1 of the examiner's twelve points of comparison.

# Transparent Photographs

A CAREFUL COMPARISON of the signatures in Figures 1 and 2 shows that, although they are similar, the questioned signature is not exactly like any of the standards.

In this case, there is absolutely no suspicion that the questioned signature is a tracing, and no transparent photograph is necessary.

## Section 10

# Markings on Photographs

F OR HIS DEMONSTRATION, the examiner will have the photographer photograph the questioned and standard signatures with a metric ruler placed beneath the signatures on the face of the specimens, as shown in Figures 7 and 8.

When the examiner receives the mounted photographs for his questioned document case, he should have the forensic photographer, if he hasn't already done so, place his mark of identification on the back of each one. The examiner will also place his own mark of identification on them.

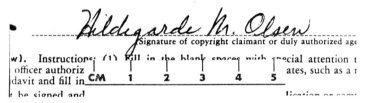

*Figure 7. The questioned signature photographed with a metric ruler on its face.*

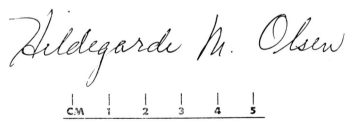

*Figure 8. One of the standards photographed with a metric ruler on its face.*

80

*Section 11*

# Mounting Exhibits

AFTER THE PHOTOGRAPHS are properly mounted, as set forth in Part II, Section 11, the exhibits are identified on the border.

The examiner will need for himself 20 by 24 inch mounted photographs of the questioned and standard signatures to use as charts for his demonstration in court.

It is also very effective to overwhelm the observers by producing 20 by 24 inch charts of each of the twelve points of comparison, individually, as shown in Figure 9.

*Figure 9. An overwhelming illustration of one of the twelve points of comparison.*

# Classification of Twelve Points of Comparison

Eᴀᴄʜ ᴏғ ᴛʜᴇ ᴛᴡᴇʟᴠᴇ ᴘᴏɪɴᴛs of comparison is cut out from the duplicate photographs of the questioned and the standard signatures, and pasted side by side in parallel columns as shown in Figure 10.

In this position, with the points of comparison placed close together, even the untrained eye can recognize at once the twelve points of similarity.

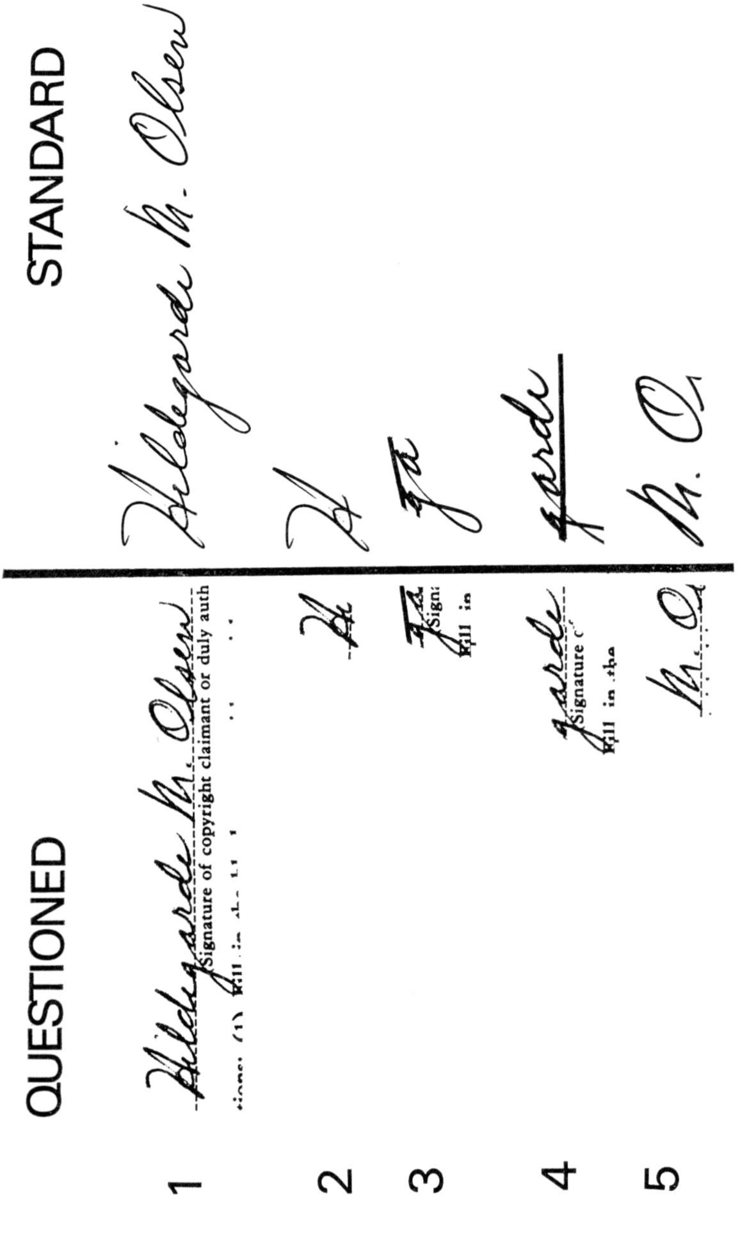

STANDARD

QUESTIONED

1　Hildegarde M. Olsen
Signature of copyright claimant or duly auth

2

3　Sign:

4　aarde
Signature o

5

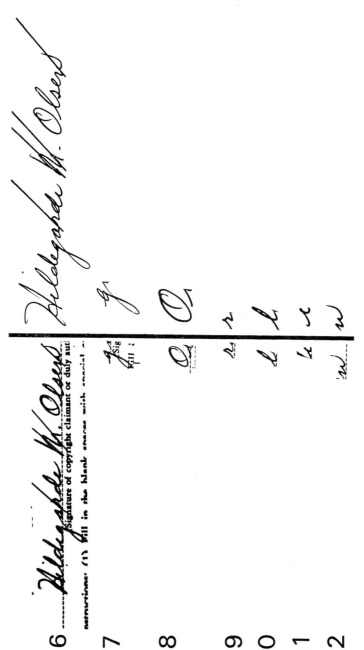

Figure 10. Classification of twelve points of comparison side by side in parallel columns.

# Presentation in Court of the Proof of the Fact

Rᴇᴀᴅʏ ᴡɪᴛʜ ʜɪs ᴄᴀʀᴇꜰᴜʟʟʏ ᴘʀᴇᴘᴀʀᴇᴅ exhibits, the handwriting examiner will demonstrate the twelve points of comparison to those who are to decide the matter in court.

Although he will emphasize the twelve points of similarity, as shown in his exhibit of their side by side classification, the examiner will weave into his presentation the many other reasons for his basis of opinion, as set forth in Section 2 of this sample demonstration. For example, he will point out the similarity of the unique capital *M,* which is a strong point of comparison even though it was not one of those characteristics selected for classification.

His presentation will be a systematic recount of the facts he had discovered during his precourt analysis of the questioned and standard signatures. Each of the facts given to the court orally will be supported by the visual exhibits furnished by the examiner.

In demonstrating the *uniformity* of the questioned writing (Point 1) the handwriting analyst will call attention to the fact that the unusually light upstroke of the *H* has not been retouched. The omission to correct an obvious ink failure or, in this case, a sweeping stroke that barely touches the paper, is an indication of genuineness.

The analyst will explain to the observers that anything about a handwriting which shows evidence that the writer wasn't thinking about the mechanics of forming the strokes is evidence of genuineness. A forger is self-conscious when he forms strokes of a writing other than his own; the act does not come naturally. On the other hand, when a writing indicates that it was done unconsciously, it is always strong evidence of genuineness.

Although it can be concluded that a signature containing a combination of naturally written characteristics is genuine — because it is illogical to contend that all of these would be present in a forgery — the examiner will point out that, nevertheless, these characteristics will vary in any given group of signatures.

A certain extent of *variation* is, in fact, evidence of genuineness. The ordinary forger doesn't allow for natural variation. He concentrates on making all the strokes as much alike as he possibly can. This fact can be brought to the notice of those in court when the handwriting analyst is demonstrating Point 3, *Size and Proportion*. A slight variation in size and proportion is also an element of genuineness.

Finally, the examiner will point out the principle underlying the identification of a questioned signature. Like any other thing which has a great number of possible variations, the identity is made by a systematic comparison of all the elements (in handwriting, the strokes) which all together make up the conclusion.

It is the *combination* of measurements and characteristics that help to identify a handwriting — a combination mathematically beyond mere chance. The appearance or omission of one characteristic may be ascribed to coincidence but, as the points of comparison mount, the probability of coincidence melts away.

*Section 14*

# Conclusion

I.s.q.d. is not meant to be a shortcut to handwriting identification. As any experienced examiner knows, there is no shortcut; questioned document investigation requires long hours of tedious study. Instead, this system is a scientific method of examining a questioned writing by breaking it down into its fundamental strokes and comparing them *stroke by stroke* with the genuine writing.

One weakness of the law of questioned documents down through the ages is that it has been based primarily upon what has been written in various books, rather than upon a scientific system based on research. I.S.Q.D. is based on the principles of the science of Graphoanalysis, which has had over a half century of research and experiment.

The examiner is not asked to take the principles of I.S.Q.D. as unquestioned truth. The real proof of this system of handwriting identification is in the examiner's testing it out for himself. Guided by the scientific principles of Graphoanalysis, the handwriting examiner can be as sure of his analysis, in any questioned document case, as a fingerprint or voiceprint specialist can be sure of his conclusion.

LIBRARY
STEPHEN F. AUSTIN STATE UNIVERSITY
NACOGDOCHES, TEXAS

# Bibliography

1. BAKER, J. NEWTON: *Law of Disputed and Forged Documents.* Charlottesville, Michie, 1955.
2. BUNKER, M.N.: *Handwriting Aanlysis.* Chicago, Nelson-Hall, 1959.
3. BUNKER, M.N.: *Graphoanalysis: General Course, Books 1-10.* Springfield, I.G.A.S., Inc., 1955.
4. BUNKER, M.N.: *Graphoanalysis: Post Graduate Course, Lectures 1-25.* Springfield, I.G.A.S., Inc., 1961.
5. COOKE, T. DICKERSON: *The Blue Book of Crime,* 24th ed. Chicago, Applied Science, 1961.
6. DEPARTMENT OF JUSTICE: F.B.I. LAB.: *They Write their own Sentences.* Washington, U.S. Government Printing Office, no date.
7. GIEBELHAUSEN, JOACHIM (Ed.) : *Manual of Applied Photography.* Munich, Karpf, 1961.
8. HARING, J. VREELAND: *The Hand of Hauptmann,* Plainfield, Hamer, 1937.
9. OSBORN, ALBERT S.: *Questioned Documents,* 2nd ed. Albany, Boyd, 1929.
10. OSBORN, ALBERT S.: *The Problem of Proof,* 2nd ed. New York and Albany, Matthew Bender, 1922.

# Index

201438